Functional English: speaking and listening

Emma Darley and Helen Darley

Acknowledgements

United Kingdom: Folens Publishers, Waterslade House, Thame Road, Haddenham, Buckinghamshire HP17 8NT.
Email: folens@folens.com

Ireland: Folens Publishers, Greenhills Road, Tallaght, Dublin 24.
Email: info@folens.ie

Editors: Kate Greig and Kayleigh Buller

Layout artists: Planman Technologies

Illustrations: Katy Dynes

Cover image: Kurt Gordon/istockphoto

Cover design: Martin Cross

First published 2008 by Folens Limited.

Every effort has been made to contact copyright holders of material used in this publication. If any copyright holder has been overlooked, we should be pleased to make any necessary arrangements.

British Library Cataloguing in Publication Data. A catalogue record for this publication is available from the British Library.

ISBN 978-1-85008-383-2

Contents

Introduction

Specials! *English* have been specifically written for teachers to use with students who may struggle with some of the skills and concepts needed for Key Stage 3 English. The titles are part of a wider series from Folens for use with lower ability students.

Each book in the series contains ten separate units covering the topics needed to complete the theme of the book. Each unit has one or more photocopiable Resource sheets and several Activity sheets. This allows the teacher to work in different ways. The tasks are differentiated throughout the book and offer all students the opportunity to expand their skills.

The teacher's notes give guidance and are laid out as follows:

Objectives
These are the main skills or knowledge to be learned.

Prior knowledge
This refers to the minimum skills or knowledge required by the students to complete the tasks. As a rule, students should have a reading comprehension age of 7 to 10 years and should be working at levels 2 to 4. Some Activity sheets are more challenging than others and you will need to select accordingly.

QCA and NC links
All units link to the QCA Schemes of Work and the NC for English at Key Stage 3 and the Northern Ireland PoS.

Background
This provides additional information for the teacher, expanding on historical details or giving further information about this unit.

Starter activity
Since the units can be taught as a lesson, a warm-up activity focusing on an aspect of the unit is suggested.

Resource sheets and Activity sheets
The Resource sheets, which are often visual but may also be written, do not include tasks and can be used as stimulus for discussion. Related tasks are provided on Activity sheets.
Where necessary, keywords are included on the student pages. Other keywords are included on the teacher's notes pages. These can be introduced to students at the teacher's discretion and depending on the students' ability.

Plenary
The teacher can use the suggestions here to recap on the main points covered or to reinforce a particular idea.

Assessment sheet
At the end of the book, is an assessment sheet focusing on student progress. It can be used in different ways.
A student can complete it as a self-assessment, while the teacher also completes one on each student's progress. They can then compare the two. This is useful in situations where the teacher or classroom assistant is working with one student. Alternatively, students can work in pairs to carry out peer assessments and then compare the outcomes with each other. Starting from a simple base that students can manage, the assessment sheet allows the student to discuss their own progress, to consider different points of view and to discuss how they might improve, thus enabling the teacher to see the work from the students perspective.

Teacher's notes

Explanation skills

Objectives

- To understand the main skills needed for explanations
- To understanding the need for effective structure when talking

Prior knowledge

Students should understand connectives and connective phrases.

English Framework links

Yr 7 Speaking and Listening 3, 4; Yr 8 Speaking and Listening 4; Yr 9 Speaking and Listening 1

Scottish attainment targets

Strand – Listening in Groups: Level A, B, C, D, E

National Curriculum in Wales links

Oracy: Range1, 2, Skills 3

Northern Ireland PoS

Talking to include debate, role-play, interviews, presentations and group discussions.

Background

In many different walks of life, students will be required to confidently use explanations within their speech. This section explores some of the more common techniques that they could transfer into most tasks and contexts, and shows students the need for effective structure within their speech. Not only will this section help to improve their verbal ability, but these skills could also be transferred into a writing task, where students are required to record their explanations.

Starter activity

Ask students to think about their day so far and try to list as many different examples of when they heard somebody explaining something. These examples should be discussed and students should be asked to think about what helped make any of these explanations successful or effective; try to steer their discussion towards considering the structure of the speech.

Resource sheets and Activity sheets

To help make this skill more approachable, students could think about explanations in terms of four key rules. Resource sheet, 'The four rules of explanation', offers four of the more common techniques that students could use within explanations, and offers suggestions about how to transfer these ideas into their own speech. Students should keep referring to this sheet throughout the lesson.

Focussing upon the first rule: to start an explanation with a clear opening; students should look at the Activity sheet, 'Successful starts'. This helps to enforce the need for a logical, clear structure at the beginning of their explanations.

Activity sheet, 'What's wrong with this?', demonstrates how confusing an explanation can be when people do not follow the four rules. The students could listen to the speech on this sheet and discuss why this explanation is confusing.

To draw students' attention back to the four rules, the Activity sheet, 'You're the teacher', provides students with an opportunity to use the rules as a mark scheme. The speech on this sheet could be read out and students could give it a possible mark out of four.

Finally, students could attempt to construct their own explanation. They could follow the task on the Activity sheet, 'Have a go at your own explanation'. The students could be asked to plan a small, two minute talk for this task, using this sheet as a framework, or guide for how to structure their speech.

Plenary

Without looking at their sheet, students could be asked to recite the four rules of explanation.

The four rules of explanation

The rules	Tips to help you
You should always start any explanation with a clear, strong opening that tells the other person what you are going to explain.	You may want to start your explanation with a phrase such as 'To begin with, I would like to explain to you...'
Your explanation must be well structured. If your explanation is muddled it can be very confusing for your listener.	Perhaps you could use some connectives in your speech to help structure your ideas, saying words like 'firstly', 'secondly' or 'another reason', etc.
You always need to finish your explanation with a concluding section. This has to sum up your important points.	You could perhaps start this part with a phrase such as 'in conclusion...'
When explaining your main points, you should try to use the present tense throughout.	You should always use verbs in the present tense such as 'I think it is important'.

Successful starts

When explaining something to a listener, you must always make sure that the opening part of your speech tells the listener what your explanation will be about.

☞ Have a look at the following conversations. Some are successful because they make it clear what the explanation is about; others are confusing because they do not make it clear. Put a tick in the box next to the people you think use an effective introduction.

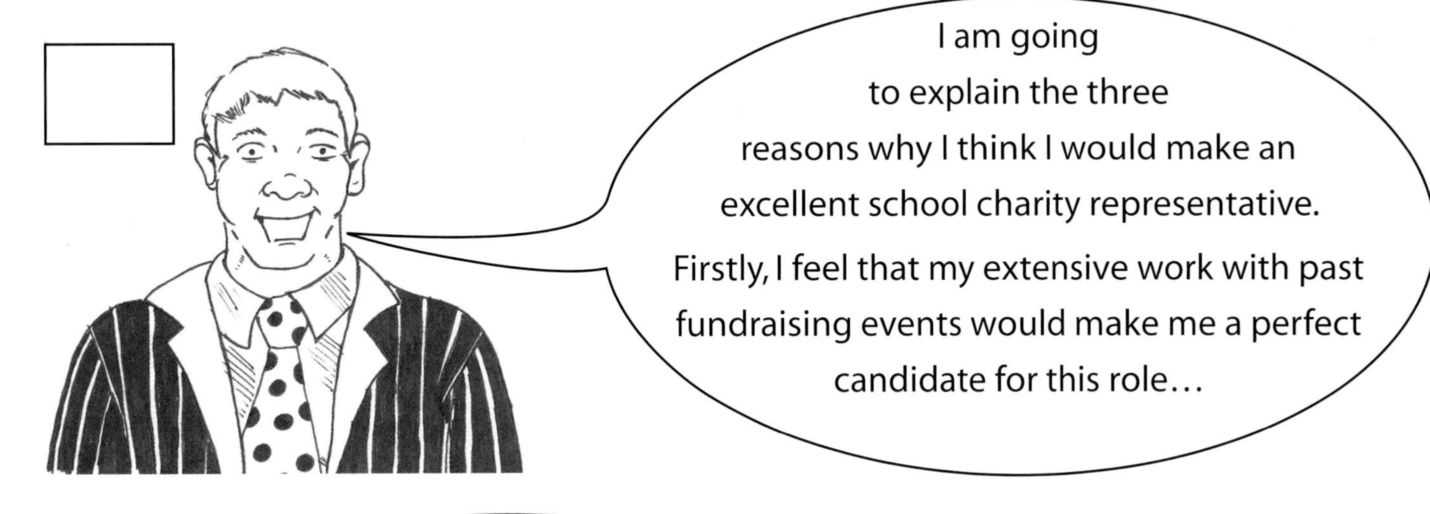

It needs to stay open. Without this money we will face great difficulties. It is important that we see how crucial this money is to our school. Did I mention that it is for the benefit of the whole community? I also meant to explain why we need to raise money to keep the sports club open.

The main reason why we should all try to stay fit is linked to our health and I would now like to explain why. A healthy heart will prevent all sorts of nasty illnesses and diseases such as heart failure, high blood pressure and respiratory problems.

Activity sheet – Explanation skills

What's wrong with this?

☞ Read the following example of a student's speech. He has been asked to explain what a typical day at his school involves. Your teacher will read this speech out loud. After you have listened to it, discuss what you think is wrong with the speech.

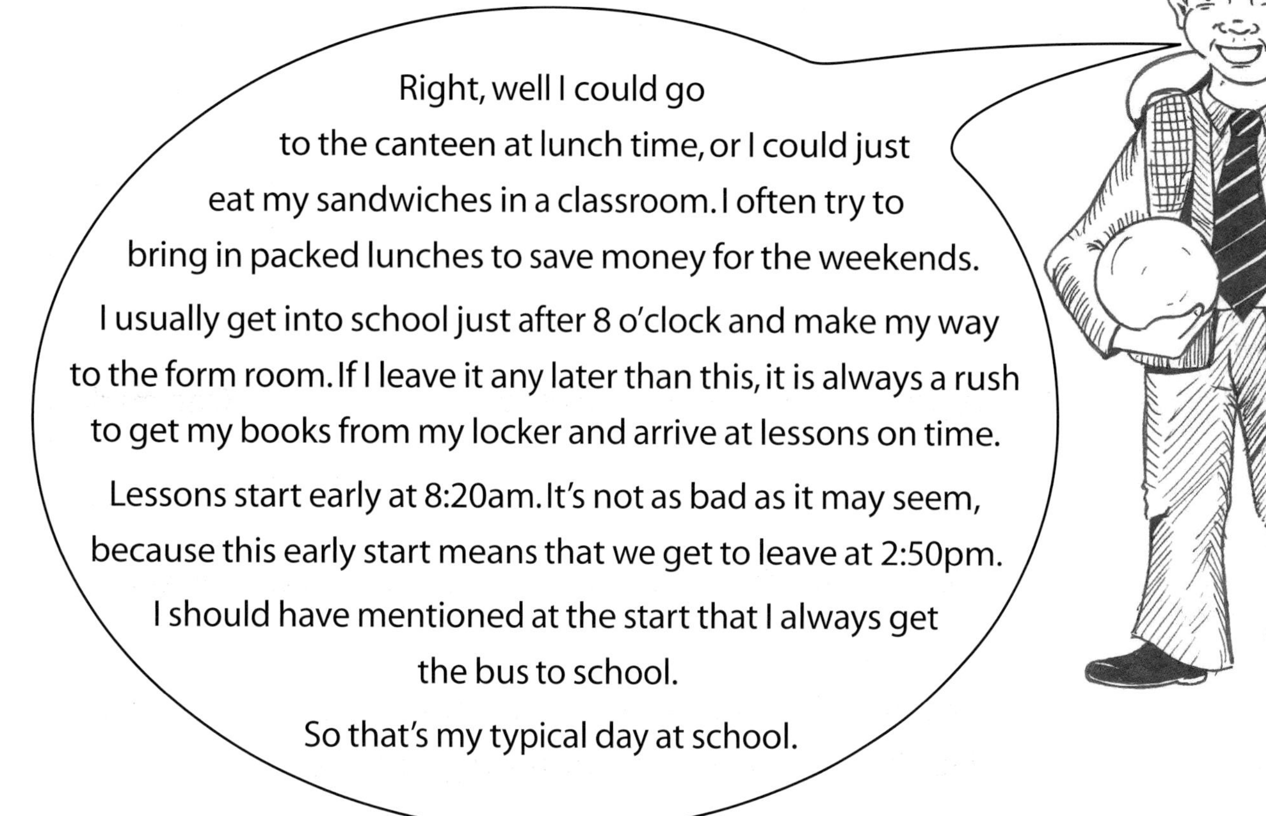

Activity sheet – Explanation skills

You're the teacher

☞ Listen to the following explanation. Using the four rules of explanation as your mark scheme, try to decide whether you would give it full marks.

Mark Scheme

The rules	Points
It must begin with a clear, strong opening that tells the other person what the explanation is about.	One mark
The explanation must be well structured.	One mark
The explanation needs to finish with a concluding section.	One mark
Throughout the explanation, present tense should be used.	One mark

To begin with, I would like to explain why I think the amount of homework we currently receive should be reduced.

Firstly, students already spend much of their time completing homework tasks instead of playing sports, becoming involved in school clubs and socialising with friends. Too much homework could make us antisocial.

Another reason why I feel it should be reduced is that it can make us less interested in school. If a student gets home, tired after a long day at school, and they are forced to complete more work, they could soon become demotivated and disinterested in the subject.

In conclusion, it does seem that homework could have a negative effect upon children.

Have a go at your own explanation

☞ Explain what a typical day at your school involves.

I would like to explain…

There are two main details I think you should know about my day…

Firstly…

Secondly…

In conclusion…

Teacher's notes

Listening for specific information

Objectives

- To understand strategies to use when listening for specific information in a conversation

English Framework links

Yr 7 Listening 6, 7; Yr 8 Listening 6, 7; Yr 9 Listening 4

Scottish attainment targets

Strand – Listening for information, instructions and directions: Level A, B, C, D, E

National Curriculum in Wales links

Oracy: Range 2, Skills 8

Northern Ireland PoS

Listening actively and reporting back.

Background

Listening for information is a skill students need to use in schools and in their personal and work life. By teaching this skill, it helps students to be able to locate information both verbally and in written text, because it encourages students to focus upon keywords. It also teaches them to be more accurate and precise with their listening, so that they are only taking the relevant parts of information away with them, encouraging them to spot a focus or a purpose for their listening. By looking at the sequence of information, such as recorded messages, students can start to predict the type of information they will hear.

Starter activity

In pairs, students should perform a short role-play. One student is a person who phones up their local bus station for bus times in their local area. The other person is the telephone operator who gives the information. The pair should improvise this conversation and the person asking for the information should jot down any important information they hear. After this activity, discuss with the class any important techniques they used to ensure that they recorded the relevant information.

Resource sheets and Activity sheets

After discussing any listening techniques the students used in the starter exercise, they should be given the Resource sheet, 'How to listen for information'. This provides students with a list, which they can add to, of techniques they could use to help their listening skills, especially when listening for specific information.

To teach students how to listen to relevant information, they need to be aware of the need to write down, or remember keywords which will be relevant to the conversation. Activity sheet, 'Flight information', provides students with a listening task. The task requires students to only record information relevant to the task. Before they start the task, students should underline any keywords or phrases that they will have to listen out for in order to record the correct information. Once students are ready, you should read out the script on Resource sheet, 'Teacher script (1)'.

The Activity sheet, 'Stolen credit card', provides students with another activity where they must focus upon specific information relevant to the task. However, this task is not as structured or as directed as the previous task, and this will focus upon the students' ability to listen and record the relevant information. A script is provided for the activity on the Resource sheet, 'Teacher script (2)'.

Plenary

The activity used in the starter activity should now be repeated, only this time the pair should swap roles, so that they each get a chance to record the information.

How to listen for information

- Try to listen out for main points, or keywords.

- Before you listen, get it clear in your mind what you are listening for. Perhaps write these keywords or points down and look at these whilst you listen.

- If it is possible, it might help to jot down keywords on a piece of paper as you listen to the information, so that you remember what you have heard.

- Try to list, in note form, what you hear. If the speaker numbers their information, you should try to remember these details in number order, or jot them down in this order.

- If you are unsure, always ask politely for the speaker to repeat the information.

Flight information

☞ You are about to go on holiday to Spain and need to phone the airport information line to check details about your flight. When you phone this number you have to listen to a recorded message which contains all the information you need about your flight. You do need to listen carefully, because the message also contains information about other flights. You will hear this recorded message soon.

Before you listen, you need to be aware of the following important information:

You are flying from Newcastle to Malaga on flight number BGT342.

When you listen to the information, you should try to find the answers to the following questions:

What time will the flight leave?

When must you arrive at the airport?

How many pieces of hand luggage can you take on the flight?

What is your maximum luggage weight allowance?

What is the telephone number for the customer service line?

Teacher script (1)

Thank you for calling British Globe Travel. The following information relates to all our flights leaving the United Kingdom on Monday 16th June. Please listen carefully for the information concerning your particular flight.

Flight BR4515 departing from Manchester to Alicante will leave on time at 1900 hours. Please ensure that you are at the airport two hours before departure. You are only permitted to take one piece of hand luggage per person on the aircraft and your maximum weight allowance for this flight is 20kg.

Flight BGT342 departing from Newcastle to Malaga will leave at 1500 hours. Please ensure that you are at the airport two hours before departure. You are only permitted to take one piece of hand luggage per person on the aircraft and your maximum weight allowance for this flight is 18kg.

Flight BGT56 departing from Aberdeen to London Heathrow has been cancelled. Please call our customer information line for more information concerning this cancellation.

We ask that all passengers read our travel terms and conditions (which can be found on our website) for further information about your flight.

Thank you for calling British Globe Travel. For further information please call our customer service line on 0561 345 773.

Stolen credit card

You think your credit card has been stolen from your bag. You have phoned the bank and have to listen to a recorded message which tells you what you should do now.

☞ Listen to the message and jot down the important information.

Teacher script (2)

Thank you for phoning Harlington Bank. You are now through to the security information line. If you have lost or had your credit card stolen you need to listen to the following advice.

If your credit card was lost or stolen you need to phone our cancellations team on 0676 765 345 immediately to freeze your credit card. This will prevent anybody from using your card without your knowledge. This line is open 24 hours.

Before phoning the cancellations team you should have the following three pieces of information to hand: your account number, your card number and the reference number from a recent card statement.

If you suspect that your credit card was stolen you should also phone your local police station to report the theft. We will require the crime reference number that the police will issue you with.

As a security measure, please be aware that none of our team will ever ask for your password details and under no circumstances should you pass on these details to anybody else.

Thank you for calling Harlington Bank. If you would like to speak to a member of our customer service team please dial 675 now.

Teacher's notes

Following instructions

Objectives

- To listen to and follow instructions
- To pick out the relevant information

Prior knowledge

It may be useful for students to have looked at commands and imperatives.

English Framework links

Yr 7 Listening 6, 9; Yr 8 Listening 7

Scottish attainment targets

Strand – Listening for information, instructions and directions: Level A, B, C, D, E

National Curriculum in Wales links

Oracy: Range 2, Skills 8

Northern Ireland PoS

Listening actively and reporting back.

Background

Following instructions is an important communication skill, whether they be written or oral instructions. Many confusions and mistakes occur when students fail to listen properly to instructions. Therefore, this section attempts to teach students how to listen actively to commands, and how to pay attention to the more important information being conveyed in instructions.

Starter activity

In pairs, students should be given a piece of paper, and one person must instruct the other to make a paper aeroplane. The person making the aeroplane can only follow the instructions given. Once the task has been completed, students should be asked to consider how successful they were in giving instructions and how well they listened to the instructions.

Resource sheets and Activity sheets

To test students' ability to listen to instructions and follow them correctly, they could be given a map exercise. Students must pretend that they have asked a person in the street directions to the supermarket. The instructions on the teachers script on the Resource sheet, 'The village script', should be read out to the students and after reading it out, issue each student with a map from the Activity sheet, 'The village'. Students should try to mark the correct route to the supermarket, trying to remember the directions they have heard. After students have completed this activity, they should be asked to discuss strategies they use to successfully remember instructions.

Students should be aware that, when following commands or instructions, they need only listen and select the relevant information. The Resource sheet, 'The doctor', contains two imaginary speeches from a doctor to a patient. Read each speech in turn, and students must pretend that they are the patient listening to the instructions. After they have heard each one, they must recount the instructions they need to follow. It is important to encourage the students to omit the unnecessary details and only recount the instructions: this will help to improve their ability to listen to the relevant information.

Finally, to improve students' ability at listening to certain pieces of information and concentrating upon what is being said, they should pretend that they are new employees on their first day of a new job. Their manager is reading out the fire drill procedures from the Resource sheet, 'Employees script'. Whilst listening to the instructions, they should answer the questions on Activity sheet, 'A fire drill'.

Plenary

Repeat the exercise used in the starter activity, only this time each pair should swap roles so each student has a chance of instructing.

Resource sheet – Following instructions

'The village' script

Starting from the post office, you need to turn left and walk down Manor Drive; you will pass a church on your left. You will then go over a small bridge and past the village school. Just after the school, you will need to take the second road on your right, it's called Jupiter Road. You walk straight down this road and you will pass the village park. Just after the park you need to take the third road on the right. The supermarket is on this road.

Activity sheet – Following instructions

The village

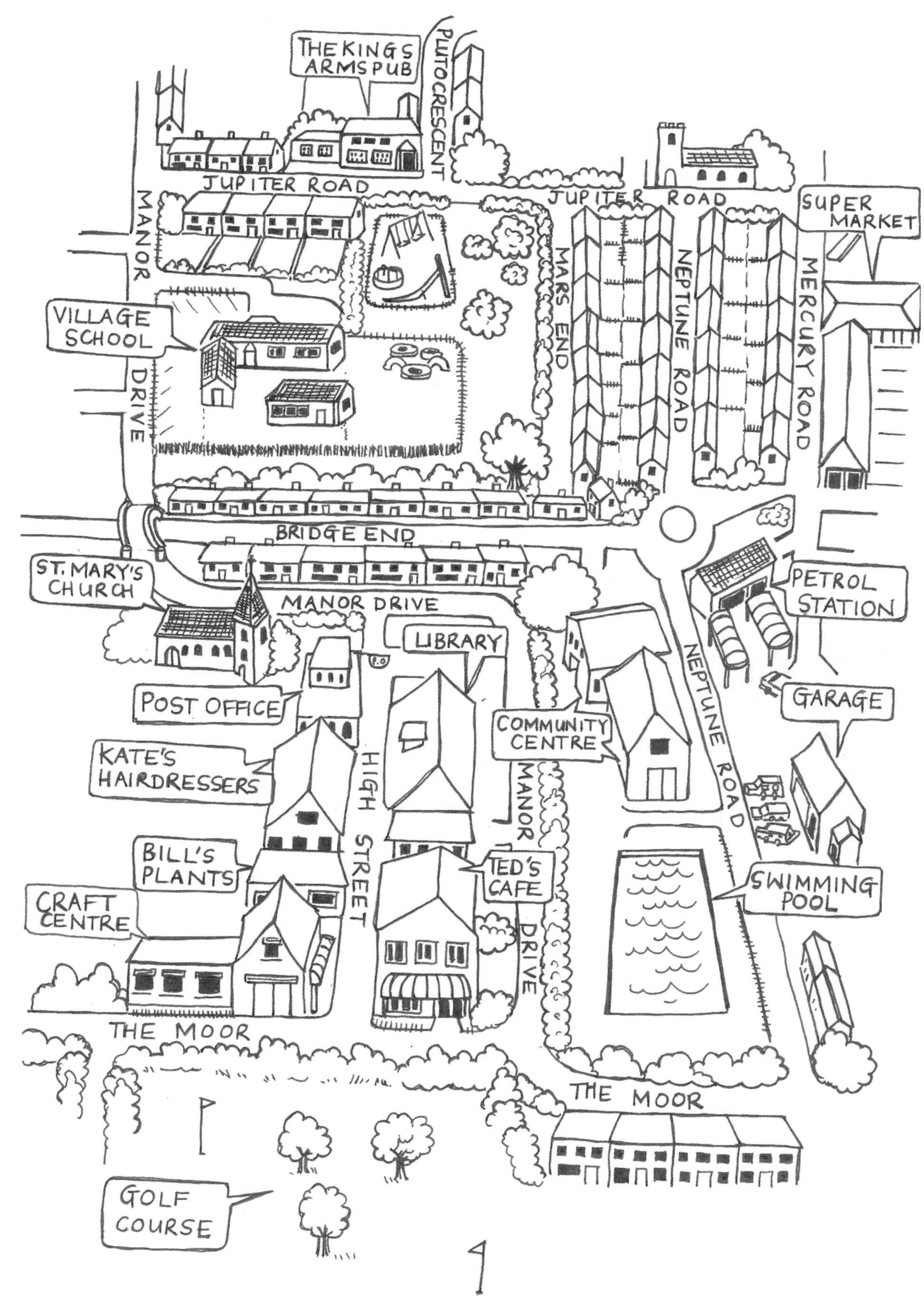

The doctor

Patient One

Well, having listened to your symptoms it is clear that you are suffering from flu. I am not going to prescribe you any antibiotics because they will have no effect on the flu virus. Instead, you need to stay in bed for at least three days. You must drink lots of fluids. You can take painkillers for your sore throat and headache and make sure that you have lots of warm drinks. You may also want to buy some throat sweets or lozenges to ease your sore throat.

Patient Two

From listening to what you have told me, and looking at the rash on your arms, I think that you have what's called Prickly Heat. I don't need to prescribe anything, but you can buy a treatment at the chemist. You should buy some calamine lotion and rub this all over the rash. This will help the itching. If it does not clear up within three days you need to come back and see me and I can then give you a stronger cream. However, at the moment, it looks like calamine lotion will do the trick.

Employee's script

Could all employees please listen to this information very carefully and record the information on their sheets. It is important that you look over this information, so that you know what to do in the case of an emergency.

If you hear the fire alarm, you will need to exit from the nearest door: in your case you will exit from Door C. This will take you to the outside of the building. You will then walk across the gardens, past the monument and head towards the car park.

When you reach the car park, you will then have to stand at assembly point 2. Your team leader will then record your name on the attendance list.

You will only be allowed back into the building when the fire brigade have finished. You must not take any of your personal belongings with you as they may slow you down.

You must walk at all times and stay calm. Never take the lift.

A fire drill

Pretend you have just started working in an office and are now being told the emergency procedures should there be a fire alarm.

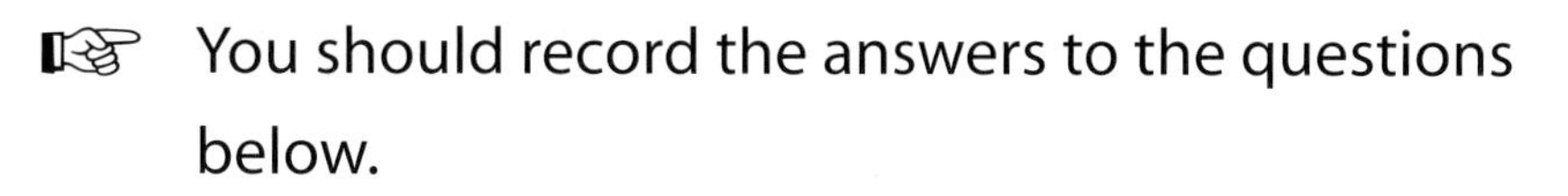

☞ You should record the answers to the questions below.

In the event of hearing a fire alarm, what door should you use to exit from?

Once outside, what route should you take to get to the car park?

What assembly point will you have to stand at, once you reach the car park?

Who will record your name?

When will you be allowed back into the building?

Should you use the lift?

Teacher's notes

Responding appropriately to comments

Objectives

- To express opinions, both in agreement and contrasting

English Framework links

Yr 7 Speaking 5

National Curriculum in Wales links

Oracy: 1, Range 1

Northern Ireland PoS

Expressing meaning, feelings and viewpoints.

Background

In all situations, be it at school or outside, students need to be able to respond appropriately to comments during a conversation. Whilst it seems a basic skill, some students struggle to form responses that are appropriate and convey their own ideas. This unit attempts to show how students could use their own opinions, within their responses, to develop their communicative abilities.

Starter activity

Students could be asked to think about a conversation they have had where they responded inappropriately. For example, they may think of an argument they have had with a family member. Students should be encouraged to think about what the definition of an 'inappropriate response' is, and try to talk about the effect of such responses on a conversation.

Resource sheets and Activity sheets

To begin, students could be asked to look at the Resource sheet, 'How should I respond?'. The students should look at speaker B's responses in the three conversations and discuss whether they are appropriate or not. For the inappropriate comments, students should be encouraged to think about the reasons why it is the wrong way to respond and the effect it has upon the conversation.

So that students can both respond appropriately and convey their own opinion, Resource sheet, 'Phrases for you to use', provides students with a list of sentences they may want to use when completing the next speaking exercises.

Activity sheet, 'Conveying your own point of view in response to other people's views', gives students the opportunity to respond to a conversation, with an appropriate response that shows their own agreement. The sheet provides planning space, so that students can prepare their point of view before speaking aloud.

It is just as important that students learn how to offer a contradictory or alternative viewpoint during a conversation. Activity sheet, 'How to show that you disagree', offers students the chance to do this. Students should keep referring back to the bank of phrases they have on the Resource sheet, 'Phrases for you to use', when completing these activities.

A final technique students could use during a conversation could be to use some of the speaker's words when making their own contributions. This will help make their responses relevant. Activity sheet, 'Building upon other people's responses', teaches students how to build upon other people's responses and contributions.

Plenary

Referring back to the discussions of the plenary, students could now be asked to define the term 'an appropriate response'. Hopefully their definition may now include some of the theory learnt in this lesson.

How should I respond?

A: I think the issue of global warming is a very serious one and something that we should all be worried about.

B: You're wrong. Be quiet.

A: I think the issue of global warming is a very serious one and something that we should all be worried about.

B: I agree.

A: I think the issue of global warming is a very serious one and something that we should all be worried about.

B: I do agree with your point that it is a serious issue. It seems that many people are worried about the state of the environment and I share your concerns that it is something we need to think about.

Phrases for you to use

I strongly agree with your idea…

I would have to disagree with your previous point…

In reference to your idea, I would agree…

I would like to offer an alternative argument…

I, too, share similar ideas about…

Whilst I understand what you are saying, I would like to point out that…

In response to your points, I would like to offer an alternative viewpoint…

Conveying your own point of view in response to other people's views

Speaker One: I think the idea that the government are proposing, to move away from using SATs as a way to assess children's ability in both primary and secondary schools, is a very good idea. Children are tested far too often, they sit exams at ages 7, 11 and 14 and it's too demanding for youngsters. I think it would be a good idea to scrap these exams and instead focus upon learning, rather than testing.

☞ Try to respond to this speaker. You should try to think of the answer you would give which shows that you also agree with what the speaker has just said to you. You might like to write down some ideas to help prompt your speech.

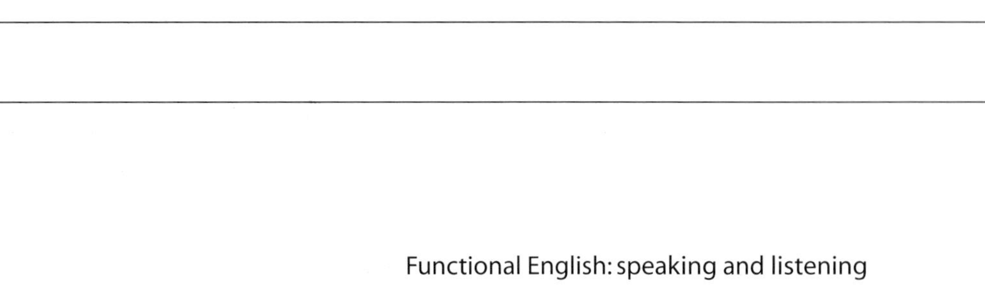

How to show that you disagree

Speaker One: I think the idea that the government are proposing, to move away from using SATs as a way to assess children's ability in both primary and secondary schools, is a very good idea. Children are tested far too often, they sit exams at ages 7, 11 and 14 and it's too demanding for youngsters. I think it would be a good idea to scrap these exams and instead focus upon learning, rather than testing.

☞ Now try to respond to this speaker, only this time you must show that you disagree with what is being said. You should write down some ideas about what you will say. Remember, when you disagree, you should not be argumentative, but stay polite when discussing your ideas.

Building upon other people's responses

When responding to someone's ideas, it is a useful idea to try to pick up on some of their words or ideas.

☞ Look at the following conversation. Speaker B has tried to use some of Speaker A's words when responding. Underline any examples of this.

Speaker A: I think the decision to open a supermarket in the local village is a bad choice. Just think about the damage it would do to the nature reserve, not to mention the litter and the increase of traffic into the area.

Speaker B: I agree with your point that it would damage the local nature reserve, but I would like you to explain why you think the increase of traffic in the area would be a negative thing.

Speaker A: Because it would cause more congestion, residents would not be able to park and the roads would be more dangerous.

Speaker B: I understand what you are saying, but I must pick up on your point about residents not being able to park. The parking situation would not change; in fact, it would improve, because the supermarket plans to open a large car park on the waste ground.

Teacher's notes

Making clear contributions

Objectives

- Understanding how to make clear responses during conversations

English Framework links

Yr 7 Speaking 1, 4; Yr 8 Speaking 5

National Curriculum in Wales links

Oracy: Range 2, Skills 1, 2

Northern Ireland PoS

Talking to include debate, role-play, interviews, presentations and group discussions.

Background

One of the greatest problems students can have when performing speaking and listening tasks is to make unclear contributions. This can often be due to nervousness, or can sometimes show a lack of understanding. This unit aims to help students to make precise, clear responses during conversations; especially dialogues that take place within a more formal setting.

Starter activity

As a class, try to play the game Chinese Whispers. One person should whisper a sentence to the person sitting next to them and then that person, whispers the same sentence to the next person and so on, until the last person to hear the sentence has to say it aloud. Hopefully, the final sentence will have changed from the original sentence. Talk to the class about the importance of making contributions within a sentence clear, because unclear contributions can make a sentence confusing, or can change the conversation's meaning completely; much like what often happens in Chinese Whispers.

Resource sheets and Activity sheets

Students could look at the example of a conversation on Activity sheet, 'The bank', in which one speaker makes confusing responses. In pairs, students could read the conversation together and discuss what they think the customer is doing wrong. Discuss the customer's unclear, confusing answers and the fact that she keeps answering questions with questions. Students could be asked to improvise their own version of the conversation; only this time the customer should make clear responses to the questions asked by the bank manager. An alternative version of the conversation is provided on Resource sheet, 'The correct way of responding'.

Students could then be given the chance to have their own conversations, in which they must provide clear answers. In pairs, students should be given Activity sheet, 'A refund'. One of the students should take the role of the customer; the other should be the store manager. The students should improvise the conversation, using the questions provided. They should both think about the clear responses that the customer needs to give, in order to receive a refund.

To further the students' understanding of how to make clear, yet polite contributions in exchanges, students could improvise another scenario. In pairs, one student should take the role of the waiter; the other should take the role of the unhappy customer. The Activity sheet, 'Dealing with an unhappy customer' and the Activity sheet, 'Being an unhappy customer', provide the students with an outline of what they must convey. Students must formulate their own responses.

Plenary

Students could be asked to create their own scenarios of a conversation where clear responses are needed. They should be asked to perform two versions of it: one which shows unclear contribution, and the second which shows the correct version.

Activity sheet – Making clear contributions

The bank

☞ Have a look at the following conversation: it is between a bank manager and a customer. The customer does not make very clear contributions to the exchange. What is she doing wrong?

Bank manager: After having looked at your bank statement, it seems that you are spending more money each month, yet your wage has not increased. Your debts are becoming large. Do you think you could try to decrease your spending?

Customer: Well, maybe, don't know, not sure really.

Bank manager: But looking at your past purchases, are all the things you buy each month really necessary?

Customer: They sometimes are, but sometimes not.

Bank manager: So, you could save some money?

Customer: Do you think so? Not sure? What do you think?

Bank manager: Yes.

Resource sheet – Making clear contributions

The correct way of responding

Bank manager: After having looked at your bank statement, it seems that you are spending more money each month, yet your wage has not increased. Your debts are becoming large. Do you think you could try to decrease your spending?

Customer: Yes, it's something I really do need to do. At the moment I am spending far more than I have.

Bank manager: But looking at your past purchases, are all the things you buy each month really necessary?

Customer: They sometimes are but, on the whole, no you're right, I am buying far too many luxury items.

Bank manager: So, you could save some money?

Customer: I definitely could cut back on some items, yes.

Bank manager: Excellent.

Activity sheet – Making clear contributions

A refund

☞ Pretend you are a customer in a supermarket who has to return a faulty mobile phone; you would like a refund. These are the questions you will be asked by the store manager. Try to prepare some clear answers to the questions. You should make sure your answers clearly convey the correct information.

Have you used the product?

____

____

____

How did the phone break?

____

____

____

Do you want a refund or a replacement?

____

____

____

When did you buy the product?

____

____

____

Do you have any proof of purchase?

____

____

____

Dealing with an unhappy customer

- You are the head waiter in an expensive restaurant and have been called over to talk to an unhappy customer.

- You must remain calm and polite to the customer at all times.

- Try to agree with everything that the customer tells you.

- You need to politely explain that it is not restaurant policy to offer free bottles of wine, but you can give a discount off the final bill.

- You should always address the customer using Sir or Madam.

- You must keep apologising for their unhappiness.

Activity sheet – Making clear contributions

Being an unhappy customer

- You have called over the head waiter because you are unhappy with the portion sizes in an expensive restaurant.

- You should try to make your point, but not be rude or aggressive.

- You should try to ask the waiter for a free bottle of wine, to make up for the small portion sizes.

- You should try to listen to everything the waiter tells you and clearly explain the reasons why you are unhappy with your meal.

Teacher's notes

Asking questions to attain correct information

Objectives

- To understand the different types of questions and their effects in conversation

Prior knowledge

It may be useful, but not essential, for students to understand closed and open questions.

English Framework links

Yr 7 Speaking 1; Yr 8 Speaking 5; Yr 9 Speaking 3

National Curriculum in Wales links

Oracy: Range 2, Skills 11

Northern Ireland PoS

Listening actively and reporting back.

Background

This unit attempts to show students how to use different types of questions and their function in conversations. Students are usually good at asking questions; however, they sometimes do not realise the different types of questions that they already have at their disposal and the effect of using different question types when trying to attain correct information.

Starter activity

Ask students to imagine that they have been asked to interview their favourite pop star/actor/celebrity. They must draw up a list of three questions that they would like to ask. After students have compiled their list, explain that the focus of this lesson is questions and explain that these three questions will be referred to at the end of the lesson.

Resource sheets and Activity sheets

Using Resource sheet, 'The different types of questions', students should be introduced to the variety of questions they have at their disposal. Students should look at the sheet and be asked to compile their own examples for each type of question. The Activity sheet, 'What type of question is being used?', then tests students' understanding of the questions.

Students could then be introduced to the differences between open and closed questions. Activity sheet, 'Using open questions to attain more information', highlights the drawbacks of always using closed questions and requires students to convert each closed question into an open one.

The Activity sheet, 'Using reflective questions if you are unsure', then offers students a technique to use if they are feeling unsure or confused during a conversation. The sheet contains an exercise to reinforce students' understanding of this question type.

Finally, Activity sheet, 'Now try your own question', could be used as a revision of all the different question types. In pairs, students should follow the scenario and improvise a conversation, paying particular focus upon the different question types and the reason for using such questions.

Plenary

Referring back to the three questions that the students devised during the starter activity, the students should hopefully be able to identify the different question types that they have used. Some may also want to change some of their questions, if they have chosen to use closed questions.

Resource sheet – Asking questions to obtain correct information

The different types of questions

Open questions: These questions are useful because they often encourage speakers to answer at length, rather than just saying yes, or no. Open questions often start with some of the following words: who, what, why, how, when.

Closed Questions: Are questions that require a yes or no answer. No other details are needed.

Hypothetical Questions: This is a question to make the speaker think about an event in the future, or to think of a situation in theory, rather than actually doing it. For example: 'If you won the lottery, what would you do?'

Reflective Questions: These can be used to check that you have understood what the person has just said. For example, 'So just to clarify, you think it is a bad idea?'

Leading Questions: This type of question almost helps the listener to answer. For example: 'You will be going out tonight, won't you?'

What type of question is being used?

☞ Have a look at the following different questions and try to identify what type of question is being used. Look at each one and decide whether it is an open, closed, reflective, leading or hypothetical question.

He is going to eat the steak, isn't he?

Where was the party?

If you didn't have the flu, would you go to the party?

Did you like the party?

You weren't going to put that dress on, were you?

So just to repeat, you will be going out tonight?

If you were a teacher, would you be strict?

Just let me check I've got this right: you do want to make the booking?

How did you get there?

Do you like it?

Using open questions to attain more information

Have a look at the following list of closed questions. Closed questions are sometimes a problem in conversations because they mean that the speaker only answers with one word. Therefore, when trying to find out more information, you should try to use open questions that require longer, more detailed answers.

☞ Try to convert these closed questions into open questions. You may want to add in the words how, what, where, when. The first one has been done for you…

Closed Question	Open Question
Are you going to do that homework?	*When are you going to do that homework?*
Will you tidy your bedroom?	
Would you like to go there?	
Do you want to go on holiday?	
Will you go to bed now?	
Are you going to fix the door today?	
Can you put the book away?	
Did you manage to get there on time?	
Did you do much today?	

Using reflective questions if you are unsure

If you are talking to somebody and you are unsure about what they have just said, or don't understand, you should try to use reflective questions. For example, look at the following conversation. The second person has not really understood what has been said, so uses a reflective question to help.

Speaker One:	**Speaker Two:**
I thought that the matter was resolved on Friday, but it seems that this matter is still being carried on today and I'm unsure about why this matter is still being discussed.	So, just to clarify, you thought that the matter was resolved?

☞ Look at the next two conversations and try to add a reflective question into the box for Speaker Two. This question should help the second speaker to understand what has just been said.

Speaker One:	**Speaker Two:**
I really wanted to go out on Saturday but I know that Darren was only free on Friday and Susie was available on Monday.	

Speaker One:	**Speaker Two:**
I put the clothes in the wardrobe, but before going into the wardrobe I went into the bathroom, the bedroom and the study. I've even found the new shoes.	

Now try your own questions

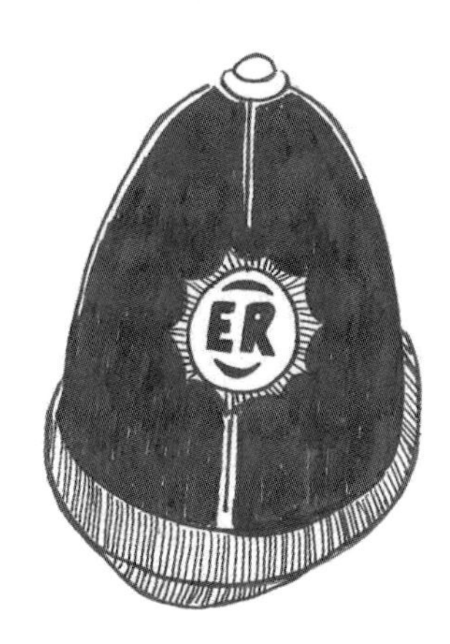

☞ You need to work in pairs for this exercise.

Person One: You are going to be a police officer.
Person Two: You are going to be the teenager who is being questioned by the police officer.

Scenario

The police officer is questioning the teenager about a crime that has been committed. Graffiti has been found on a wall in the local town centre and the teenagers name has been mentioned as the person responsible. The police officer needs to ask the teenager as many open questions as possible to try to find out whether the teenager is responsible for the crime. Remember, the police officer must not use any leading questions, or try to put words in the teenager's mouth.

In pairs, you should improvise this scene. You need to think about the questions the police officer would ask, perhaps you should write them down beforehand.

Person One/Police Officer: You should try to avoid using closed questions – you won't get much information from using these.

Person Two/Teenager: If you're the teenager, you may want to ask some reflective questions, to make sure you understand exactly why you have been brought into the police station and why you are being questioned.

Teacher's notes

Understanding opinions expressed by others

Objectives

- Understanding how to identify opinions
- Understanding how to listen for relevant opinion
- Understanding how to look for disguised opinions

Prior knowledge

It would be helpful if students understood the differences between facts and opinion.

English Framework links

Yr 7 Speaking; Yr 8 Speaking; Yr 9 Speaking

Scottish attainment targets

Strands – Listening for information, instructions and directions: Level A, B, C, D, E

National Curriculum in Wales links

Oracy: Range 2, Skills 5

Northern Ireland PoS

Listening actively and reporting back.

Background

Trying to teach students how to understand opinions can be a difficult task. One way of teaching it would be to ensure that students understand how to identify an opinion and the differences between that opinion and a fact. Once students have a firm understanding of what an opinion is, they could then move on to looking at how some speakers either try to disguise or avoid using their own opinion. This unit attempts to introduce these concepts to students in order to improve their ability to both listen to, and communicate, their own opinions during conversations.

Starter activity

To start, ask the students to write down a list of five opinions they have about school. Explain that these opinions can be about anything in school they have a belief, or view about. Once they have completed this task, explain that this list will be referred to at the end of the lesson.

Resource sheets and Activity sheets

The first Activity sheet, 'Is it a fact or an opinion?', provides students with an introductory exercise aimed at showing the differences between facts and opinions. Students should read the variety of statements and decide whether they are referring to a fact, or an opinion.

Once students understand the differences between facts and opinions, they could be given the chance to identify them being used as part of dialogue. Activity sheet, 'Which is which?', shows several statements that students should look at and decide whether they are factual or not.

It is then important to show students that opinions can often be disguised, to look like facts. Activity sheet, 'A conversation with a head teacher', shows a conversation in which the speaker is trying to hide, or avoid using their own opinion about a subject. Students have to analyse the conversation in terms of the opinions expressed.

Students should then be taught the importance of listening to opinions during conversation and Activity sheets, 'Finding out people's opinions – Person A and B', gives students the chance to perform a practical exercise where they must listen to each other talk. In pairs, students should follow the tasks on the two Activity sheets: one student should be given the role of questioner and the other student will answer their questions using the information provided. The questioner is required to only listen out for the correct opinions, ignoring any irrelevant details.

Plenary

Referring back to the list of five opinions that the students compiled at the start of the lesson, students should now check that they have written five opinions, rather than facts. Ask the students to explain the differences between fact and opinion.

Is it a fact or an opinion?

☞ Read the following statements and try to decide whether each one is describing a fact or an opinion. Tick the correct box once you have decided.

		Fact	Opinion
1	Something which is definitely true	☐	☐
2	A personal belief	☐	☐
3	Something which could be supported by evidence	☐	☐
4	Something that someone believes in	☐	☐
5	Something that a person could have made up	☐	☐
6	Something that you can not argue with	☐	☐
7	Something you may want to argue with	☐	☐

Activity sheet – Understanding opinions expressed by others

Which is which?

☞ Have a look at the following different extracts: some are examples of facts, and others are examples of people's opinions. Try to decide which is which. Colour the facts in one colour and the opinions in another colour.

I thought the team played well.
The team scored three goals.
The film lasted three hours and ten minutes.
The film was far too long.
The man seemed to be a little uncomfortable.
The man was 40 years old.
I think it would be a good idea.
The law was passed in 1976.
Did you see his concert? He was amazing on stage.
His concert was viewed by thousands of people.

A conversation with a head teacher

☞ Sometimes, during conversations, it can be difficult to work out what people's opinions are, especially if they try to avoid answering questions. Have a look at the following conversation between an interviewer and a head teacher. Try to underline any opinions the head teacher expresses about the school council's new idea.

Interviewer: Please could you tell me, head teacher, what your opinion is of the school council's idea that students should be given more free time, rather than homework?

Head Teacher: I can understand why the council would favour such an idea, being that the council is made up of mainly school pupils; therefore it would be advantageous to most of them.

Interviewer: Yes, but what do you think about this idea?

Head Teacher: As I said, it would be an idea that would suit students.

Interviewer: Yes, but what is your own opinion about the idea, as a teacher?

Head Teacher: As a teacher, I think it is important that the school council have a chance to air their views.

Interviewer: You've not answered my question: what's your opinion about the new idea that students should receive less homework?

Head Teacher: Well, as a teacher I think the idea needs a little more development. I understand that students feel that they have a lot of homework, but it's the only way to ensure that they cover the whole syllabus and so can enter their exams confident and prepared.

Finding out people's opinions – Person A

☞ **Person A:** You are responsible for asking your partner the following questions about flying. You must listen to their answers carefully, and jot down any opinions that they may give in the space below each one. Remember, you are only interested in their opinions about flying.

Question One: Why don't you like flying?

Question Two: Have you always had a fear of flying?

Question Three: Do you think you could ever enjoy flying?

Finding out people's opinions – Person B

☞ **Person B:** You are responsible for answering the three questions that your partner asks you. You must only answer each one with the following information don't add in any other information.

Question One:
You must answer their first question with the following facts and opinions:

There are many ways of travelling.

Thousands of people use other forms of transport.

I think it's because I'm frightened of something going wrong.

Question One:
You must answer their second question with the following facts and opinions:

I have flown three times.

I have been on a long haul flight.

I think my fear goes back to childhood.

Question One:
You must answer their third question with the following facts and opinions:

I may try going on the ferry next year.

There are many different ferry companies to choose from.

I don't think flying is something I'll ever like.

Teacher's notes

Using appropriate language

Objectives

- To understand the differences between standard and non-standard English
- To understand how to change the formality of a conversation, depending upon the context

Prior knowledge

It may be useful if students understand the idea of formal and informal.

English Framework links

Yr 7 Speaking 3; Yr 8 Speaking 3; Yr 8 Speaking 2

National Curriculum in Wales links

Oracy: Range 2, Skills 2

Northern Ireland PoS

Talking to include debate, role-play, interviews and group discussions.

Background

Students will probably be aware of the need to change the formality of their language, depending upon the context of the conversation. However, to reinforce this idea and to extend their understanding of it, it would be useful for students to understand the concepts of standard and non-standard English. Once students fully understand these two levels of formality, they can change their own register accordingly.

Starter activity

Students should be asked to list three situations where they have to talk using a formal register, e.g. talking to a judge. They should then list three situations where they would use more informal language, e.g. talking on the phone to a friend. Encourage students to think about the differences in their language when talking in these different registers. Try to encourage students to think about how they change certain words or avoid using slang in certain situations.

Resource sheets and Activity sheets

Students should be made aware that their language and responses should change according to the context in which the exchange occurs. Activity sheet, 'The children and the policeman', shows how responses can change according to the authority or position of speakers. Students should look at the three different extracts of a conversation between a policeman and youths and decide which extracts show an appropriate use of language.

When teaching how to use language appropriately, it would be a good idea to ensure that students understand the differences between standard and non-standard English. Activity sheet, 'Standard and non-standard English', helps students to understand the difference between the two forms of language.

To help further students understanding of non-standard English, Activity sheet, 'Using the correct language', helps students to understand that, when talking to somebody in a position of authority, informal or colloquial language should be avoided. The task requires students to change any informal language into standard English.

The final Activity sheet, 'Speaker A', gives students the chance to practise using appropriate language in a formal context. In pairs, one student should pretend to be the head teacher and the second student is a pupil who has been summoned to his office. The students should follow the tasks on the sheet and improvise a conversation, using the correct, formal language required for such a scenario.

Plenary

Pick out one student to define, in their own words, the following terms:

Standard English
Non-standard English
Colloquialisms

Activity sheet – Using appropriate language

The children and the policeman

☞ Have a look at the following extracts of conversations between a policeman and a group of children he has met in the park. Which conversation shows an appropriate use of language?

Conversation One:

Policeman: Where have you just been?

Child One: Why should we tell you?

Policeman: I beg your pardon?

Child One: Whatever.

Conversation Two:

Policeman: Have you been anywhere near the supermarket tonight?

Child Two: No, we have been here all evening.

Policeman: Do your parents know where you are?

Child Two: Yes, they are picking us up in ten minutes.

Conversation Three:

Policeman: There has been a report of a group of children, matching your description, stealing from the supermarket.

Child Three: Do I look bothered?

Policeman: Would you prefer to answer these questions at the police station?

Child Three: Love to, mate.

Standard and non-standard English

☞ Have a look at the following phrases and identify which are examples of standard English and which are examples of non-standard English. Circle the phrases you think are non-standard English.

Example One:	Good morning your Majesty. G'day matey.
Example Two:	What'ya up to. What will you be doing today?
Example Three:	Fancy a brew? Would you like a cup of tea?
Example Four:	Don't matter to me. I am really not interested.
Example Five:	Yeah? Yes.
Example Six:	It was proper good that film. I enjoyed that film.
Example Seven:	Innit a shame hey? It is a shame.

Using the correct language

When you are talking to somebody in a position of authority, or somebody who you should be polite and respectful towards, you should try not to use any slang or colloquialisms (informal language) within your speech.

☞ Have a look at the following piece of a dialogue. Try to change all the underlined examples of slang and colloquialisms into more formal, appropriate language. Use the boxes provided to insert the alternative word. One has already been done for you.

Well, I am sorry Prime Minister, but it really was a whopping great big mistake on my behalf. I never knew you'd go psycho about it. It's just I've been really scatty and ditsy lately. I knew that those papers were important, but for some reason I just chucked them out with the rubbish. Whoops. I could probably go and search through the bins if the things mean that much to you. Are you really hacked off at me?

Sorry.

Activity sheet – Using appropriate language

Speaker A

☞ You should pretend that you are a head teacher and you have summoned a student to your office. You suspect that the student is responsible for throwing an egg at a teacher's car. Improvise a conversation with the student. Remember, you are in a position of authority and would mostly use standard English within your speech. Within your conversation, you should ask the following three questions:

1 Why did you throw the egg?

2 Do you realise the consequences of your action?

3 Do you feel any remorse?

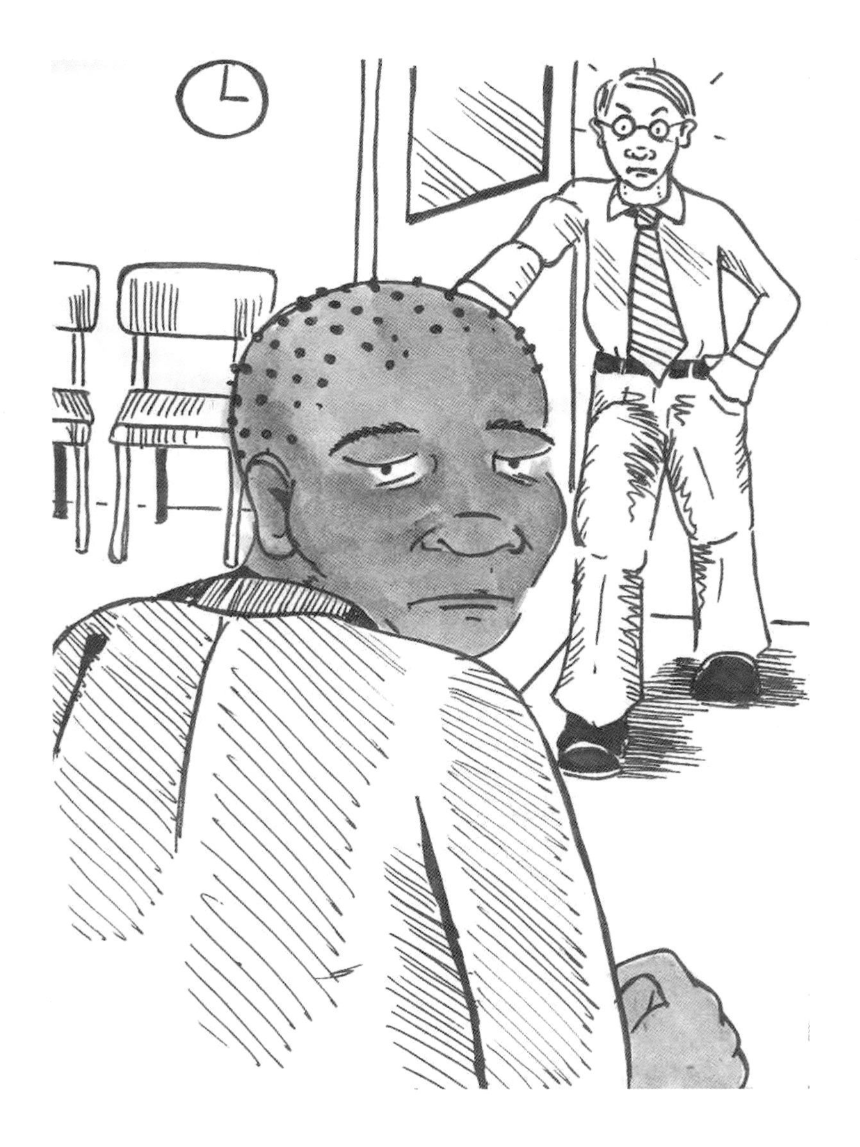

Activity sheet – Using appropriate language

Speaker B

☞ You should pretend that you are a student who has been summoned to your head teacher's office. You have been spotted throwing an egg at a teacher's car. You should improvise a conversation with the head teacher. Remember, you will be speaking to somebody in authority and so you should mostly use standard English within your speech. Within your conversation, you should listen to the head teacher's questions and try to use these three phrases within your speech. Make sure you do not use any slang or colloquialisms.

1 I have no idea why I performed such a ridiculous act.

2 I fully realise the consequences of my action.

3 I feel guilty about the act.

Teacher's notes

Knowing your audience

Objectives

- To understand how to select language to suit the needs of an audience

English Framework links

Yr 7 Speaking 3; Yr 8 Speaking 1; Yr 9 Speaking 1

National Curriculum in Wales links

Oracy: 1, Range 2

Northern Ireland PoS

Talking to include debate, role play, interviews, presentations and group discussions.

Background

When preparing a speech, students should be aware that their language choices can help to target their intended audience. This unit aims to help students to realise that.

Starter activity

Ask the students to write down the following word: 'wooing'. Ask students to define the term and whether they know of any modern alternatives, for example: going out, courting, etc. Encourage students to realise that different words are associated with different generations of people, and when preparing a speech for a certain audience, you need to think about the choice of language used.

Resource sheets and Activity sheets

To introduce students to the idea that language changes, depending upon the listener, Activity sheet, 'Who are they talking to?', provides a task to show how language choices can be used to target specific listeners/audience.

The Activity sheet, 'Language choices for specific audiences', leads to understanding of how certain individual words can be used to address your listener. Once students understand the significance of individual words within their speech, they could be asked to complete the task on the Activity sheet, 'A charity event'. The task requires students to select certain words they may wish to insert into an imaginary speech. This technique is an excellent planning device, when students have to prepare speeches, and it helps to ensure that the speech stays on-task and relevant.

For the next activity, students should work in pairs. One student should take on the imaginary role of a travel agent. Using Activity sheet, 'The speaker', they should imagine that they have to deliver a speech to an annual conference of other agents. The student is asked to devise the opening paragraph to this speech, using words suitable to this audience type. The second student should take on the role of audience member, and listen to this opening paragraph. Using Activity sheet, 'The listener', students should listen carefully to the word choices used by the speaker and record them on the sheet. This activity will help students not only to plan the correct language for their intended audiences, but also encourage them to listen closely and attentively.

Plenary

Referring back to the activity used in the starter, ask students to come up with their own examples of words that would perhaps mean nothing to the older generation. Emphasise the point that, when preparing a speech, language choice is very important so that you convey the correct meaning to your intended audience.

Who are they talking to?

☞ Look at the following examples of conversations. They are all conversations which have a particular audience. See if you can tell who that audience is.

Conversation A

So, if we could all strive to really push the results up this year. It's been a tough year and we've had many interruptions, but nevertheless, it's now time to knuckle down and revise. It's only for three weeks and then you can enjoy your long holiday.

Conversation B

Ladies and gentlemen, we now have bread reduced on the bakery aisle, from 39p to 10p. There are many other great offers to be found around the store. Why not have a look in our new clothing section, found at the back of the store?

Conversation C

Welcome aboard and thank you for choosing us. We kindly ask that you refrain from smoking and place all luggage under your seat or in your overhead locker. Seatbelts should remain fastened throughout the take-off.

Language choices for specific audiences

When trying to address a specific audience, there may be certain word choices you should use. For example, a teacher addressing students may use words associated with study and work. Have a look at the following conversations and underline any words or phrases which are specific to the particular audience. The first example has been done for you.

1. **A teacher addressing a group of students**

Your revision needs to be done regularly. After each session, you should always read back over your notes and write down any important points. This will ensure success within your forthcoming exams.

2. **A detective addressing a group of policemen**

The crime rate in this area is particularly low, and in the past three years we have only made 25 arrests. The criminal gangs seem to have moved out of the area and there seem to be only minor offences committed.

3. **A bank manager talking to his staff**

Make sure that you always check the interest rates when selling the loans and credit cards. It is important that customers who have large overdrafts are not given too much credit, otherwise we run the risk of debt.

4. **A librarian talking to a lender**

Yes, if you have a look in the fiction section, just next to the autobiographies I think you will find his latest book. It is only out in hardback at the moment.

Activity sheet – Knowing your audience

A charity event

☞ Imagine you have been asked to give a speech at the annual staff party of a large charity who raise money for the homeless. The speech must congratulate the workers of the charity for all their hard work and the money that they have raised over the last two years. Try to compile a list of words and phrases that you might use, within the speech, which would be appropriate for this particular audience. One has been added to get you started.

worthy cause

The speaker

You are addressing a group of travel agents. You are delivering a speech at their annual conference. The speech is entitled: 'The best holiday destinations for your customers'. You should write the opening paragraph of this speech, trying to use as many words as you can that are specific to this particular audience of people. You will have to read this speech out to your partner.

☞ 1 To help get you started, write down ten words that are specific to this particular audience. The first one has been done for you…

1 resort	6
2	7
3	8
4	9
5	10

☞ 2 Now write the opening paragraph to this speech. Remember, you must include all the words that you have listed.

____

____

____

____

____

____

____

____

____

Activity sheet – Knowing your audience

The listener

☞ You are about to hear the opening of a speech. Listen to it carefully and then fill in the following boxes. You may need to ask the speaker to repeat the speech so that you don't miss anything!

1. Who is the audience for this speech?

2. What particular words have been used in this speech that are specifically aimed at this audience? Try to record at least ten words.

Teacher's notes

Review

Objectives

- To compose spoken instructions
- To revise the use of questions in conversation
- To revise the use of appropriate language in conversation
- To revise structure within speeches

Prior knowledge

It would be useful if students have worked through the previous nine chapters

English Framework links

Yr 7 Speaking 3, Yr 8 Speaking 1, Yr 9 Speaking 1

National Curriculum in Wales links

Oracy: 1, Range 2

Northern Ireland PoS

Talking to include debate, role play, interviews, presentations and group discussions. Listening actively and reporting back.

Background

After working through the units, this section provides revision of some of the skills covered.

Starter activity

Students could be asked to briefly recap the main areas they have covered. They could also be asked to write a list of the main things they must think about when listening to important pieces of information.

Resource sheets and Activity sheets

The first Activity sheet, 'The Prime Minister', tests students' understanding of structure within their speeches. The sheet encourages students to use clear openings and conclusions, as well as incorporating sequencing connectives within their talk.

The second Activity sheet, 'Paper aeroplanes', provides students with a practical exercise to test their ability to not only follow, but compose spoken instructions.

Activity sheet, 'Who am I?', reinforces students' understanding of open questions, encouraging students to use words such as 'why', 'what' and 'when' to help devise questions that require a detailed and informative answer.

Resource sheet, 'Using appropriate language', contains a script that could be read out to the students. The script contains inappropriate phrases and words (these are all underlined). The students could be asked to stand up every time they hear an inappropriate language choice and then sit down once the language becomes acceptable.

Plenary

Use the assessment sheet to see what students have learned and what they need to work on.

Activity sheet – Review

The Prime Minister

☞ Imagine you are Prime Minister. You are giving your first television broadcast to the public. Explain some of the policies and ideas you would introduce into Britain.

Remember, an explanation has to have a clear, strong opening. What will you include in this opening? The opening must explain what the speech will be about.

Make sure that your explanation has a clear structure. Maybe you could introduce your ideas using connectives such as 'firstly' or 'secondly'. Write down two ideas for your speech.

The speech will also need a conclusion, summing up your main ideas. Write down some ideas that you could use for your conclusion.

Activity sheet – Review

Paper aeroplanes

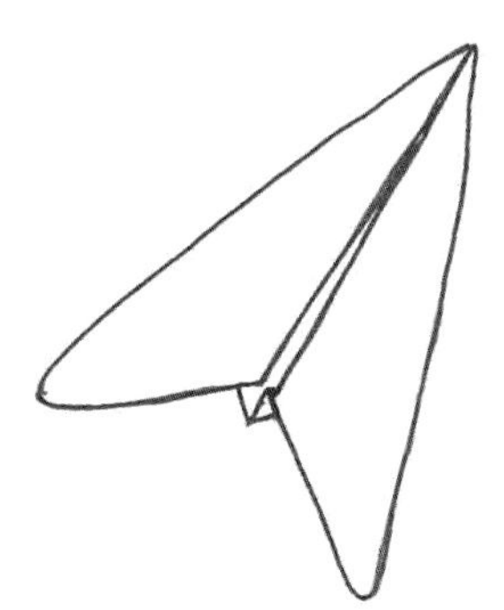

☞ Your task is to provide your partner with a set of five spoken instructions which they can follow. Once they have followed the instructions they will have built their very own paper aeroplane. Use the following space and tips to create your instructions and then you should read them out to your partner.

Remember, instructions should be clear, straightforward and precise. They should follow a logical order.

Instruction one

Instruction two

Instruction three

Instruction four

Instruction five

Activity sheet – Review

Who am I?

☞ Your teacher has picked one famous person's name. You need to try to find out what name it is. However, you are only allowed to ask three questions, and these three questions cannot be closed questions (they must not produce a yes or no response). You need to ask three open questions, which the teacher must answer. You may want to use the following words at the start of each question, to try to get information from the teacher: what, why, where.

(You are not allowed to ask the question: Who is it?)

Question one

Question two

Question three

Resource sheet – Review

Using appropriate language

This extract shows the use of inappropriate language whilst at an important job interview. The underlining has been done to show you where the applicant went wrong.

I think I would be extremely well suited to the position because of my organisational skills and my technological capabilities. I understand most computer design programmes and I reckon I could use your company's packages. I'm not being funny, but I think I'm pretty good at drawing and so would be able to cope with the marketing side of the job. I believe that I have good social skills and have loads of mates. I have some excellent referees who would be more than happy to provide references and things. I'm a confident, reliable worker who can be trusted to perform a range of tasks independently and without any problems. I'm dead honest and I wouldn't mess you around. I am passionate about my work; especially my design skills and think that you'd be well impressed with me. If you wanna give me a job I'd be really made up.

Assessment sheet

✓ Tick the boxes to show what you know or what you can do.

	Yes	Not sure	Don't know
I listen to the teacher.			
I work well with a partner.			
I can work well in a group.			

The thing that I remember most is:

____

____

I need to work on (up to three targets):

1 ______________________________

2 ______________________________

3 ______________________________

